Gustave Alexandre Eiffel

Gustave Alexandre Eiffel

teNeues

Editor in chief:
Paco Asensio

Archipockets coordination:
Aurora Cuito

Editor and original texts:
Llorenç Bonet

Photographs:
© Roger Casas

Photographs on pages 8 and 9:
© Collection Tour Eiffel 2002

English translation:
William Bain

German translation:
Bettina Beck

French translation:
Agencia Lingo Sense

Italian translation:
Giovanna Carnevali

Graphic Design / Layout:
Emma Termes Parera and Soti Mas-Bagà

Published worldwide by teNeues Publishing Group
(except Spain, Portugal and South-America):

teNeues Book Division
Kaistraße 18, 40221 Düsseldorf, Germany
Tel.: 0049-(0)211-994597-0
Fax: 0049-(0)211-994597-40

teNeues Publishing Company
16 West 22nd Street, New York, N.Y., 10010, USA
Tel.: 001-212-627-9090
Fax: 001-212-627-9511

teNeues Publishing UK Ltd.
Aldwych House, 81 Aldwych
London WC2B 4HP, UK
Tel.: 0044-1892-837-171
Fax: 0044-1892-837-272

teNeues France S.A.R.L.
140, rue de la Croix Nivert
75015 Paris, France
Tel.: 0033-1-5576-6205
Fax: 0033-1-5576-6419

www.teneues.com

Editorial project:

© 2003 LOFT Publications
Domènech 9, 2º 2ª
08012 Barcelona, Spain
Tel.: 0034 932 183 099
Fax: 0034 932 370 060
e-mail: loft@loftpublications.com
www.loftpublications.com

Printed by:
Gráficas Anman. Sabadell, Spain.

February 2003

Bibliographic information published by Die Deutsche Bibliothek
Die Deutsche Bibliothek lists this publication in the Deutsche Nationalbibliografie; detailed bibliographic data is available in the Internet at http://dnb.ddb.de.

ISBN: 3-8238-5540-9

Garabit Viaduct
Viadukt von Garabit
Viaduc de Garabit
Viadotto del Garabit

Pedestrian bridge in Girona
Steg in Girona
Passerelle à Girone
Passerella in Girona

Saint Jean Bridge
Brücke von Saint Jean
Pont de Saint Jean
Ponte di Saint Jean

The work of Gustave Eiffel (Dijon, 1832–Paris, 1923) may be seen as forming part of the positivist generation, among whose ideas we find that of sustained and unlimited progress. The great symbol of this generation is in fact the railroad because it presents an infrastructure that was bound to allow a lowering of transportation costs, a greater mobility and dynamic, and an endless number of other advantages. These advantages, it must be said, took somewhat longer than expected to become a part of quotidian reality. Jules Verne (1828–1905) incarnates the figure par excellence of the chronicler of this modern age whose heroes are engineers and whose scientists are its wise men.

This is the socioeconomic environment into which Gustave Eiffel was born. His great-great-grandfather, installed in France since 1710 and originally from Renania (Germany), had changed his unpronounceable surname, Boenickhausen, to Eiffel. His great-grandson, Gustave Eiffel's father, enlisted in the army of Napoleon and was sent to Dijon, where he would marry Catherine Moneuse. Gustave Eiffel was highly influenced by the figure of his mother, whose authoritarian character led her to take over the family bookkeeping.

Thanks to a contact arranged by his mother, Gustave met Charles Nepveu shortly after taking his engineering diploma at the École Centrale des Arts et Manufactures. Nepveu ranked high in society and had his own company. He introduced the young Eiffel into the world of bridge building, and it was thanks to Nepveu as well that Eiffel obtained the supervision of the bridge in Bordeaux, where he demonstrated his great organizational capacity and his gift of socializing with people. These were qualities that would eventually serve him well in the future company he would establish.

Gustave Eiffel was far from untalented as a businessman. He made important contacts and used to advantage his great business abilities. His career may be summed up as a spectacular progression of successes: a young man from the provinces came to be one of his country's ten most important contractors—without the least doubt the most renowned. His popularity and his good reputation were key elements in his being chosen to raise the tower that bears his name. His projects are found on all five continents, and the most spectacular ones of all are the large pieces, such as the Oporto Bridge, the Garabit Bridge, or the Statue of Liberty structure in New York (the statue itself being the work of sculptor Auguste Bartholdi). But there is also no mean number of lesser-known designs that brought the French engineer enormous benefits, such as the portable bridges which the company designed and exploited in the 1880s and which brought such high financial returns. These still span a large number of rivers in Asia and in South America.

The last 20 years of Eiffel's life were spent away from business concerns and in a fight to keep his tower from being dismantled. For this, he needed to have recourse to such sometimes conflicting arguments as national pride and the need of the city of Paris to have a communications tower (the base of which, obviously, would already exist), or a meteorological studio, an already functioning aerodynamic hangar. (His passion was studying the wind.)

The aerodynamic studies which Eiffel published were translated into other languages. They set an important precedent for the development of this nascent science to dominate the air (dating from the end of the nineteenth and the beginning of the twentieth century). He even built an aerodynamic laboratory complete with a wind tunnel where all the prototypes of French airplanes, both civil and military, would for many years be tested.

Garabit Viaduct
Viadukt von Garabit
Viaduc de Garabit
Viadotto del Garabit

Cubzac Bridge
Brücke von Cubzac
Pont de Cubzac
Ponte di Cubzac

Pedestrian bridge in Girona
Steg in Girona
Passerelle à Girone
Passerella in Girona

Gustave Eiffel (Dijon, 1832–Paris, 1923) zählte zu den Positivisten, die sich durch ihr Streben nach anhaltendem und grenzenlosem Fortschritt auszeichneten. Das große Symbol dieser Generation war die Eisenbahn, die eine neue Infrastruktur mit verminderten Transportkosten, größerer Mobilität und Dynamik sowie eine endlose Reihe weiterer Fortschritte hervorbringen sollte, die sich aber erst viel später als erwartet einstellten. Jules Verne (1828–1905) verkörperte die Figur des Chronisten dieser modernen Epoche, in der Ingenieure Helden und Wissenschaftler Weise sind.

In dieses gesellschaftliche und wirtschaftliche Umfeld wurde Gustave Eiffel geboren. Sein aus dem Rheinland stammender Ururgroßvater, der ab 1710 in Frankreich ansässig war, hatte seinen unaussprechlichen Nachnamen Boenickhausen durch Eiffel ersetzt. Sein Urenkel, Gustave Eiffels Vater, diente im Heer Napoleons und wurde nach Dijon befohlen, wo er Catherine Moneuse heiratete. Gustave Eiffel wuchs unter dem überaus starken Einfluss seiner Mutter auf, die mit ihrem autoritären Charakter die gesamten Familiengeschäfte in der Hand hielt.

Über seine Mutter lernte Eiffel kurz nach seinem Abschluss als Ingenieur an der Zentralen Kunst- und Manufakturschule Charles Nepveu kennen. Nepveu war gut situiert, besaß sein eigenes Unternehmen und er war es, der Eiffel in die Welt des Baus von Eisenbahnbrücken einführte. Ihm verdankte Eiffel die Bauleitung der Brücke von Bordeaux, wo er sein gesamtes Organisationstalent und seine Gabe zur Mitarbeiterführung unter Beweis stellen konnte. Diese Eigenschaften sollte er künftig in seiner eigenen Firma weiterentwickeln.

Gustave Eiffel war ein hervorragender Unternehmer. Er verschaffte sich wichtige Kontakte und wusste sein ausgeprägtes Gespür für Geschäfte richtig zu nutzen. Die Karriere dieses jungen Mannes aus der Provinz, dem der Sprung unter die zehn landesweit bedeutendsten Unternehmer gelang, ist spektakulär, zumal er zweifelsohne der bekannteste unter ihnen wurde. Seine Popularität und sein guter Ruf waren ganz entscheidend dafür, dass er schließlich den Eiffelturm errichten konnte. Seine Bauwerke befinden sich auf allen fünf Kontinenten. Die aufsehenerregendsten davon sind große Projekte wie die Brücke von Porto, die Brücke von Garabit oder aber das stählerne Skelett der Freiheitsstatue in New York, die von dem Bildhauer Auguste Bartholdi stammt. Es existiert aber auch eine große Anzahl von kleineren Entwürfen, die ihm enorme Gewinne einbrachten. Die tragbaren Brücken, die seine Gesellschaft in den achtziger Jahren des 19. Jahrhunderts entwarf und vertrieb, waren ein einträgliches Geschäft und sie überspannen noch heute zahlreiche Flüsse in Asien und Südamerika.

Die letzten zwanzig Jahre seines Lebens verbrachte Eiffel fernab von der Geschäftswelt und im ständigen Bemühen zu verhindern, dass sein Turm abgerissen würde. Um den Abriss abzuwenden, appellierte er an den Nationalstolz der Franzosen und überzeugte die Stadtverwaltung von Paris von der Notwendigkeit eines Fernmeldeturms, dessen Sockel ja bereits gebaut sei. Er schlug außerdem vor, den Turm als Wetterstation und als Werkstatt für aerodynamische Studien zu verwenden, da das Studium des Windes seine ganze Leidenschaft war.

Seine veröffentlichten aerodynamischen Studien wurden in viele Sprachen übersetzt und leisteten um die Jahrhundertwende unschätzbare Vorarbeit für die Entwicklung dieser jungen Wissenschaft, deren grundlegendes Ziel das Beherrschen des Windes war. Eiffel baute sogar ein aerodynamisches Labor mit einem Windkanal, in dem viele Jahre lang sämtliche Prototypen der zivilen und militärischen französischen Flugzeuge getestet wurden.

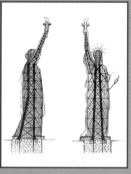

Maria Pia Bridge (Oporto, Portugal)
Maria-Pia-Brücke (Porto, Portugal)
Pont de Maria Pia (Porto, Portugal)
Ponte di Maria Pia (Oporto, Portogallo)

Eiffel Tower
Eiffelturm
Tour Eiffel
Torre Eiffel

Statue of Liberty structure
Skelett der Freiheitsstatue
Structure de la Statue de la Liberté
Struttura della statua della Libertà

Gustave Eiffel (Dijon, 1832–Paris, 1923) a inscrit son œuvre dans la perspective de la génération positiviste, comptant le progrès soutenu et illimité parmi ses idées forces. C'est le chemin de fer qui offre le grand symbole de cette génération : une infrastructure devant permettre une réduction des coûts de transport, une mobilité et un dynamisme accrus et un florilège d'avantages, dont la concrétisation se ferait attendre plus que prévu. Jules Verne (1828–1905) donne corps à la figure du chroniqueur de ces temps modernes, dont les ingénieurs sont les héros et les scientifiques les sages.

C'est dans ce cadre socio-économique que naît Gustave Eiffel. Son trisaïeul, parti de Rhénanie (Allemagne) pour s'installer en France en 1710, avait opté pour le patronyme Eiffel, abandonnant l'imprononçable Boenickhausen. Son arrière-petit-fils, le père de Gustave Eiffel et soldat dans les armées napoléoniennes, choisit Dijon où il épousa Catherine Moneuse. C'est la figure maternelle qui voit grandir Eiffel. Une femme dont la personnalité autoritaire la mènera à administrer l'ensemble des affaires familiales.

C'est justement grâce à un contact obtenu par sa mère qu'il connaît Charles Nepveu peu après l'obtention de son diplôme d'ingénieur de l'École Centrale des Arts et Manufactures. Nepveu est déjà en vue, avec sa propre société, et c'est lui qui l'introduit dans le monde de la construction des ponts de chemin de fer : il lui doit la direction de la construction du pont de Bordeaux, où il peut démontrer l'ampleur de ses capacités d'organisation et son entregent, qualités qu'il développera au sein de la future société qui portera son nom.

Gustave Eiffel fut un grand entrepreneur, sachant développer les contacts importants et jouer de son sens des affaires. Sa carrière affiche une progression spectaculaire : un jeune Rastignac devenant l'un des dix plus importants entrepreneurs du pays et, sans conteste, le plus célèbre. Sa popularité et son excellente réputation furent les éléments clés qui lui permirent d'ériger la Tour Eiffel. Ses projets peuplent les cinq continents. Les grandes œuvres sont parmi les plus spectaculaires : ainsi le pont de Porto, celui de Garabit ou la structure de la Statue de la Liberté à New York, du sculpteur Auguste Bartholdi. Pour autant, une grande diversité de créations de moindre ampleur lui ont valu d'énormes bénéfices : les ponts portables conçus et exploités par sa société dans les années 1880 furent plus que lucratifs et enjambent encore à ce jour une multitude de rivières d'Asie et d'Amérique du sud.

Les vingt dernières années de sa vie le virent éloigné des affaires, luttant pour éviter le démantèlement de sa tour. Pour ce faire, il n'économisa aucun argument, ainsi la fierté nationale, et sut convaincre la Ville de Paris de la nécessité d'une tour de communication – dont la base était déjà construite –, d'un centre d'études météorologiques, d'un atelier d'aérodynamisme en activité... Sa passion étant l'étude du vent.

Les publications de ses études aérodynamiques furent traduites dans d'autres langues, offrant des bases conséquentes au développement de cette science naissante, visant à dominer les airs, qui voyait le jour à l'orée du siècle. Il construisit même un laboratoire d'aérodynamique, disposant d'un tunnel de soufflerie, qui abriterait les essais de tous les prototypes d'avions français – civils et militaires – durant de nombreuses années.

Observatory at Nice
Observatorium von Nizza
Observatoire de Nice
Osservatorio di Nizza

Saint Jean Bridge
Brücke von Saint Jean
Pont de Saint Jean
Ponte di Saint Jean

Gustave Eiffel (Digione, 1832–Parigi, 1923) si colloca all'interno della generazione positivista, i cui ideali appoggiavano la fede incondizionata per il progresso. Il grande simbolo di questa generazione é rappresentato dalla ferrovia: un'infrastruttura che doveva rendere possibile una diminuzione dei costi del trasporto, una maggior mobilità e dinamismo e un'incredibile quantità di vantaggi che tardarono a più del tempo previsto nel rendersi realtà. Giulio Verne (1828–1905) incarna la figura del cronista del tempo moderno, dove gli ingegneri rappresentano gli eroi, i saggi e gli scienziati.

In questo quadro socioeconomio nasce Gustave Eiffel. Il suo trisavolo, trasferitosi in Francia nel 1710 dalla Renania (Germania), aveva cambiato il suo impronunciabile cognome Boenickhausen in Eiffel. Suo pronipote, immatricolato nell'esercito di Napoleone, é destinato a recarsi a Digione, dove prende come sposa Catherine Moneuse. Eiffel é cresciuto molto influnzato dalla figura della madre, il cui carattere autoritario la portò ad amministrare tutti i beni e gli affari famigliari.

Poco tempo dopo la laurea di Ingegneria presso la Scuola Centrale di Arti e Manifatture, grazie a un contatto offertogli dalla madre, conosce Charles Nepveu. Questi nutriva di ottimi contatti, aveva una compagnia propria e fu colui che lo introdusse nel mondo della costruzione di ponti e ferrovie: grazie a Nepveu ottenne la direzione della costruzione del ponte di Bordeaux, dove dimostrò gran capacità organizzativa e qualità da sviluppare nella futura compagnia che prenderà il suo nome.

Gustave Eiffel fu un gran impresario; si creò importanti contatti e seppe seguire con successo il suo fiuto per gli affari. La sua carriera é una progressione spettacolare: un giovane di provincia che arriva ad essere uno dei dieci contrattisti più grandi del paese e, senza dubbio, il più conosciuto. La sua popolarità e la sua buona reputazione rappresentarono gli elementi chiave per poter realizzare la torre Eiffel. I suoi progetti si trovano in tutti e cinque i continenti; i più importanti e di prestigio sono il ponte di Oporto, quello del Garabit e la struttura della statua della Libertà New York dello scultore Auguste Bartholdi. C'è inoltre una gran quantità di disegni che gli furono molto utili e gli portarono incredibili benefici; i ponti portatili che la compagnia disegnò e che seppe sfruttare nel decennio degli anni ottanta del XIX° secolo furono un grande business e ancora oggi permettono di attraversare numerosi fiumi in Asia e Sud America.

Gli ultimi venti anni della sua vita li trascorse lontano dagli affari e dedicò le sue energie al fine che la sua torre non venisse demolita. Con questo obiettivo dovette ricorrere ad argomentazioni tra le più diverse tra loro come per esempio l'orgoglio nazionale e convinse il Comune di Parigi sulla necessità di tenere una torre di comunicazioni, la cui base sarebbe già costruita, di fare uno studio meteriologio, un laboratorio aerodinamico in funzione. La sua passione era lo studio del vento.

Gli studi di aerodinamica che pubblicò vennero tradotti in altre lingue e confermarono un importante precedente nello sviluppo della nascente scienza che studia il movimento dell'aria, che segna il cambio del secolo. Eiffel costruì inoltre un laboratorio aerodinamico costutuito da un tunnel del vento dove si provavano tutti i prototipi di aeroplani francesi – civili e militari – per diversi anni.

Saint Jean Bridge

Bordeaux, France
1857–1860

In 1856, Charles Nepveu introduced his protégé, Eiffel, into the period's most important French railroad company. It was called the Company of the South, and at the relatively early age of 26 Eiffel was given the construction of a bridge in Bordeaux by the firm. Backed, as always, by his mentor, Eiffel would find a solution to the complicated foundation for the columns in the muddy river and use a technique introduced into France by Nepveu. What the technique consisted in was tubes of steel 3.60 meters in diameter to maintain constant pressure and expel the water infiltrations and allow the building workers a dry work area. Another technical problem was solved by the novel idea derived from the manufacture of the deck that would carry the rails, which was more than 500 meters in length. Instead of using a framework of solid pieces, Eiffel decided to use a lattice frame, a system which he himself would employ with some frequency even when he was not anymore under the auspices of Nepveu. The bridge was decorated in the neo-Gothic style, although at present only the columns remain, the entrance portico having been removed in the twentieth century.

Im Jahre 1856 wurde Eiffel von Charles Nepveu in das bedeutendste Eisenbahnunternehmen jener Zeit – die Gesellschaft des Südens – eingeführt, wo ihm im Alter von nur 26 Jahren der Bau einer Brücke in Bordeaux übertragen wurde. Unterstützt von seinem Mentor löste Eiffel die komplizierte Aufgabe der Einbettung der Pfeiler in das sumpfige Flussbett, indem er eine Technik anwendete, die eben von Nepveu in Frankreich eingeführt worden war. Sie bestand in der Verwendung von Stahlrohren mit einem Durchmesser von 3,60 Metern, innerhalb derer ein konstanter Druck herrschte, der das Eindringen von Wasser verhinderte, so dass die Arbeiter im Trockenen arbeiten konnten. Mit Hilfe neuartiger Lösungen wurde ein weiteres Problem aus dem Weg geräumt. Es bestand in der Herstellung der über 500 Meter langen Trägertafel für die Eisenbahnschienen. Statt der herkömmlichen Vollwandbalken entschied sich Eiffel für die leichtere Fachwerkbauweise und verwendete dieses System fortan selbst bei zahlreichen Gelegenheiten, als er sich schon längst nicht mehr unter der Protektion Nepveus befand. Die Brücke war im neugotischen Stil verziert, aber heute sind lediglich die Pfeiler übrig, da der Eingangsvorbau im 20. Jahrhundert entfernt wurde.

En 1856, Charles Nepveu introduit son pupille Eiffel dans la plus importante société ferroviaire française de l'époque – la Compagnie du Sud – où, à seulement 26 ans, il se voit confié la construction du pont de Bordeaux. Toujours secondé par son protecteur, Eiffel relève le défi des fondations complexes des piliers, dans des eaux boueuses, selon une technique importée en France par son propre mécène : l'utilisation de tubes d'acier de 3,60 mètres de diamètre maintenant une pression constante afin d'expulser les infiltrations d'eaux tout en permettant aux ouvriers de travailler au sec. Des solutions novatrices apportent également une solution à un autre problème technique, celui dérivant de la fabrication du plateau servant de support aux rails de la voie, sur plus de 500 mètres de long. Au lieu d'employer une armature massive, Eiffel opta pour un réseau de poutrelles, un système auquel il recourait souvent ensuite, même sans Nepveu. Le pont recevait une décoration de style néo-gothique bien que, à ce jour, seuls demeurent les piliers, le porche d'entrée ayant été supprimé au XXème siècle.

Nel 1856, Charles Nepveu introdusse il suo pupillo Eiffel nella società ferroviaria francese più importante dell'epoca la Compagnia dal Sud, dove, con solo 26 anni, viene incaricata la costruzione di un ponte a Bordeaux. Aiutato sempre dal suo talento, Eiffel risolve la complicata cimentazione dei pilastri nella fanghiglia del fiume seguendo una tecnica introdotta in Francia dal suo proprio mecenate, che consisteva nell'utilizzare tubi di acciaio da 3,60 m di diametro per mantenere una pressione costante che espullsasse le infiltrazioni di acqua e permettesse agli operai di lavorare a secco. Un altro problema tecnico risolto con soluzioni innovative consisteva nel fatto che derivava la costruzione dell'impalcatura che doveva no reggere i binari per una larghezza maggiore di 500 metri. Invece di impiegare un'armatura con l'anima piena, Eiffel decise di utilizzare travi reticolari, sistema che già lui stesso, senza l'appoggio di Nepveu, utilizzava abbondantemente. Il ponte era decorato con stile neogotico, e anche se oggi giorno rimangono solo i pilastri, perché l'arco d'entrata venne distrutto nel secolo XX.

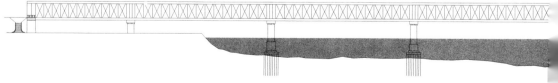

Section   **Section**
Schnitt   **Sezione**

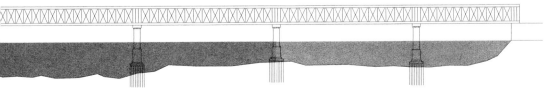

Synagogue on the Rue des Tournelles

Rue des Tournelles 21, Paris, France
1866–1867

In 1865, now working on his own, Eiffel drew up the project for the roofs of the synagogue on the rue des Tournelles, by the architect Marcellin Varcollier. But Eiffel did not take full advantage of the possibilities of a material as resistant as iron. It was the low cost he was interested in. He therefore used this material only instead of stone, although the National Library of Paris, done in the same period, already takes advantage of the structural qualities of iron for the construction of svelte columns that are capable of supporting the same weight as thicker stone piers. Here, engaged columns were used, as if they were of stone, and these are of considerable girth. A similar idea is found in the designs the company exported to South America and Asia, prefabricated in Europe, such as the churches of Tacna (Peru), Manila (Philippines) and Arica (Chile). The wood in this same region was of a very bad quality, and hence the use of iron.

Im Jahre 1865 hatte sich Eiffel bereits selbstständig gemacht und entwarf die Dächer der von dem Architekten Marcellin Varcollier in der Rue des Tournelles errichteten Synagoge. Eiffel nutzte jedoch die Möglichkeiten, die ein so widerstandsfähiges Material wie Eisen bietet, nicht zur Gänze. Eisen wurde hier eigentlich nur aufgrund seiner niedrigen Kosten verwendet und ersetzte nur den Stein als Material, obwohl bei der Nationalbibliothek von Paris, die aus der gleichen Zeit stammt, bereits die baulichen Eigenschaften des Werkstoffes ausgenutzt wurden. Diese wurden im Bau feingliedriger Pfeiler mit der gleichen Tragkraft wie der dicker Steinsäulen umgesetzt. Bei der Synagoge sind die Säulen auf die Wände aufgesetzt als ob sie aus Stein seien und besitzen einen beträchtlichen Durchmesser. Eine ähnliche Idee kann man bei Entwürfen wie denen für die Kirchen von Tacna (Peru), Manila (Philippinen) und Arica (Chile) beobachten, welche die Firma Eiffels nach Südamerika bzw. Asien exportierte, die aber in Europa vorgefertigt wurden. In jenem Gebiet war die Holzqualität überaus schlecht, so dass man für den Bau auf Eisen als Werkstoff zurückgriff.

En 1865, une fois à son compte, Eiffel projette les charpentes de la synagogue de la rue des Tournelles, de l'architecte Marcellin Varcollier. Cependant, Eiffel ne profite pas pleinement des possibilités offertes par un matériau aussi résistant que le fer. Son usage est justifié en raison de la faiblesse des coûts impliqués mais se limite à une simple substitution de la pierre. L'on remarque que la Bibliothèque nationale à Paris, à la même époque, suscite déjà l'exploitation de ses qualités structurelles. Elles se concrétisent par la construction de fins piliers, aptes à supporter le même poids que des colonnes de pierre massives. Les colonnes de cette synagogue sont adossées aux murs, comme si elles étaient en pierre, et affichent un diamètre considérable. Un questionnement similaire est observable dans les créations exportées par sa société en Amérique du sud et l'Asie et préfabriquées en Europe, ainsi les églises de Tacna (Pérou), Manille (Philippines) et Arica (Chili). La qualité relativement pauvre du bois dans cette zone imposa l'emploi du fer.

Nel 1865, quando diviene autonomo, Eiffel progetta la copertura della Sinagoga della rue des Tournelles, dell'architetto Marcellin Varcollier. Senza dubbio, Eiffel non approfitta interamente delle possibilità di un materiale così resistente come il ferro. Il suo utilizzo si giustifica per il basso costo e si limita alla mera sostituzione della pietra, non ostante il fatto che nella Biblioteca Nazionale di Parigi, della stessa epoca, si pensi a un grande sfruttamento delle sue qualità strutturali, che si materializzano nella costruzione di esili pilastri capaci di reggere lo stesso peso delle colonne di pietra. In questa Sinagoga, le colonne sono addossate ai muri, come se fossero di pietra e presentano un diametro considerévole. Un progetto simile si ritrova nei disegni che la sua società esportava in Sud America e Asia ma che si prefabbricavano in Europa, come per esempio le chiese di Tacna (Perù), Manila (Filippine) e Arica (Cile). In questa zona si registrava una pessima qualità del legno, e questa fu la ragione dell'utilizzo del ferro.

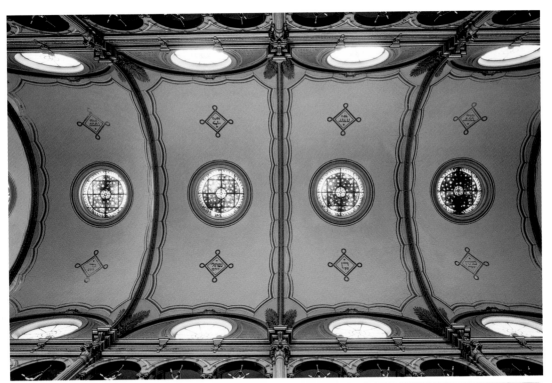

Neuvial Viaduct

Gannat, France
1869

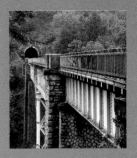

In 1869, thanks to the association with Wilhelm Nordling, an engineer of the New Orleans Company, and thanks also to an attractive cost-effective project, Eiffel managed to get the bid for the construction of two of the four bridges on the Commentry-Gannat Line, the Neuvial and the Rouzat viaducts. This would mean the first important commission for his young company. The Neuvial Viaduct measures 160.25 meters in length by 44 meters in height. It presents a very simple structure not unlike that of the Rouzat viaduct. This project is an example of two of the constants that would in the future constitute the most respected feature of Eiffel's company: the capacity to always work with the most innovative techniques and the perfection of the pieces that were manufactured there. While the design of the columns of both bridges foresaw the use of a new technique in France—cast-iron tubing in the load-bearing pieces—this was very far from keeping Eiffel from correcting the original project and improving the way of joining tubes to their mounts. And this was of course done without any delay in the execution of the work.

1869 schaffte es Eiffel aufgrund seines guten Verhältnisses zu Wilhelm Nordling, einem Ingenieur der Orleáns-Gesellschaft, und auch dank des attraktiven und kostengünstigen Entwurfs, den Auftrag zum Bau zweier der vier Brücken auf der Strecke Commentry-Gannat, also für die Viadukte von Neuvial und Rouzat zu erhalten. Dieser Auftrag war der erste von größerer Bedeutung für sein neu gegründetes Unternehmen. Das Viadukt von Neuvial ist 160,25 Meter lang, 44 Meter hoch und besitzt ähnlich wie das von Rouzat eine sehr einfache Struktur. An dem Projekt waren bereits zwei der Konstanten sichtbar, die später die am meisten geschätzten Charakteristika von Eiffels Unternehmen werden sollten: die Fähigkeit, immer die innovativsten Techniken zu verwenden, und die Perfektion der von seiner Firma gefertigten Teile. Der Entwurf der Pfeiler beider Brücken sah zwar eine in Frankreich neue Technik vor, nämlich gusseiserne Rohre für die tragenden Teile, aber das hielt Eiffel nicht davon ab, den Originalentwurf abzuändern und den Verbindungsmechanismus zwischen den Rohren und ihren Zugankern zu verbessern. Und hierbei verzögerten sich die Bauarbeiten nicht einmal.

En 1869, grâce à la relation qui le lie à Wilhelm Nordling, ingénieur de la Compagnie d'Orléans, mais aussi à un projet économique attrayant, Eiffel obtient l'adjudication de la construction de deux des quatre ponts de la ligne de chemin de fer Commentry-Gannat, les viaducs de Neuvial et de Rouzat. Il s'agit en l'occurrence de la première commande d'importance pour sa société naissante. Le viaduc de Neuvial mesure 160,25 mètres de long pour 44 mètres de haut et présente une structure très simple, semblable à celle du viaduc de Rouzat. Ce projet affiche deux constantes qui constitueront, à l'avenir, les symboles distinctifs les plus respectés de la société d'Eiffel : une capacité à travailler en s'appuyant sur les techniques les plus novatrices et la parfaite facture des pièces. Bien que la conception des piliers des deux ponts ait pu prévoir le recours à une technique nouvelle en France – des tubes métalliques fondus dans les pièces maîtresses – Eiffel se sentit toutefois libre de modifier le projet original et améliorer ainsi le mécanisme unissant tubes et montants, sans générer de délai dans l'exécution de l'œuvre.

Nel 1869, grazie alla relazione con l'ingegnere della compagnia di Orleàns, Wilhelm Nordling, e grazie a un attrattivo ed economico progetto, Eiffel ottiene l'aggiudicazione per la costruzione di due dei quattro ponti della linea Commentry-Gannat, i viadotti di Neuvial e di Rouzat. Si può considerare il primo incarico importante per la nascente società. Il viadotto di Neuvial ha 160,25 metri di longitudine e 44 metri di altezza, e presenta una struttura molto semplice, simile a quella del viadotto di Rouzat. Questo progetto evidenza due costanti che costituiranno in un futuro prossimo il segno distintivo più rispettato della compagnia: la capacità di lavorare con le tecniche più moderne e la perfezione dei pezzi di fabbrica. Anche se il progetto dei pilastri di entrambi i ponti prevede di utilizzare una tecnica nuova in Francia – tubo di ferro fuso con i pezzi maestri – questo non impedisce a Eiffel di correggere il progetto originale e migliorare il meccanismo di unione tra i tubi e i tiranti, senza che quasto implichi un ritardo nei lavori.

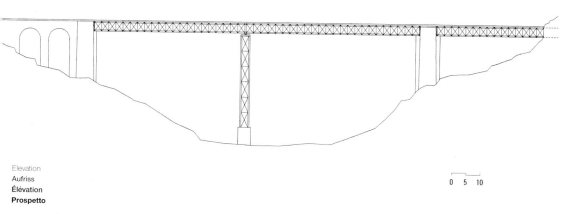

Elevation
Aufriss
Élévation
Prospetto

0   5   10

Rouzat Viaduct

Gannat, France
1869

Rouzat Viaduct is considerably larger than its sister project the Neuvial. The former is 58.90 meters high and 180.60 meters in length. But it gives an impression of a svelte profile because of the use of a simple mesh in the deck—the beams are crossed in the form of an X. A feature which is highly characteristic of both bridges is the columns, which are defined by a marked curvature where the shaft joins the stone base. This is not unreminiscent of the height progression present in the Eiffel Tower, very wide at the base and growing narrower as it rises. The bases of the pillars of the Rouzat viaduct very well demonstrate this idea of a developing progression since, being seated on a rhomboidal plan, they cover a much wider surface area. Both projects meant the beginning of the construction of large bridges with Eiffel at the helm. And this in turn would suppose the consolidation of the French engineer's firm, which thereby set out on the design of structures of great tonnage—632 tons, in the case of the Rouzat, 468 tons for the Neuvial.

Das Viadukt von Rouzat hat mit 58,90 Metern Höhe und 180,60 Metern Länge wesentlich größere Dimensionen als sein Gegenstück in Neuvial. Dennoch vermittelt es aufgrund der Verwendung eines einfachen Gitters mit x-förmig gekreuzten Balken für die Tafel den gleichen Eindruck von Schlankheit. Ein sehr charakteristisches Merkmal beider Brücken sind die Pfeiler mit ihrer ausgeprägten Bogenlinie in dem Bereich, in dem sie mit dem Steinsockel verbunden sind. Dies erinnert an die Höhenentwicklung beim Eiffelturm, der im unteren Bereich sehr breit ist und mit zunehmender Höhe immer schmaler wird. Die Pfeiler des Viadukts von Rouzat werden nach oben hin immer schlanker. Da sie von einem rhombenförmigen Grundriss ausgehen, nehmen sie unten eine wesentlich breitere Fläche ein. Beide Projekte stellten sowohl den Beginn des Baus großer Eisenbahnbrücken unter der Leitung Eiffels dar als auch die Konsolidierung seines Unternehmens, das sich so auf dem Gebiet der Planung von Konstruktionen mit großer Tonnenlast – 632 t im Falle von Rouzat und 468 t bei dem Viadukt von Neuvial – erstmals einen Namen machte.

Le viaduc de Rouzat affiche des dimensions considérablement plus conséquentes que celle de son homologue de Neuvial : 58,90 mètres de haut pour quelque 180,60 mètres de long. Il s'en déprend cependant la même sensation de finesse de par l'emploi d'un réticule simple pour le tablier – les poutrelles s'entrecroisent ainsi en formant un X. Les piliers sont les traits caractéristiques des deux ponts, arborant une courbure prononcée au point d'union avec la base en pierre. Elle n'est pas sans rappeler la progression en hauteur de la tour Eiffel, très large en sa base et s'étrécissant progressivement en gagnant de la hauteur. Les bases des piliers du viaduc de Rouzat sont un exemple remarquable de ce concept de développement progressif. En effet, assis sur un plan rhomboïde, ils couvrent une superficie beaucoup plus vaste. Ce sont ces deux projets qui ouvrent la voie de la construction de grands ponts confiés à Eiffel mais lui permettent aussi de consolider son entreprise, lancée de ce fait dans la conception de structures à fort tonnage – 632 tonnes pour Rouzat et 468 à Neuvial.

Il viadotto di Rouzat presenta delle dimensioni considerabilmente maggiori di quelle di suo fratello Neuvial: 58,90 metri di altezza e 180,60 metri di longitudine, anche se trasmette la stessa sensazione di stabilità dovuta all'impiego di una maglia reticolare semplice nell'impalcatura – le travi sono incrociate a forma di X. I pilastri sono la parte più caratteristica dei due ponti, sono definiti da una curvatura marcata nella zona di unione con la base di pietra che ricorda la progressione in altezza che presenta la Torre Eiffel, molto larga alla base e più stretta proporzionalmente all'altezza. Le basi dei pilastri del viadotto dimostrano chiaramente questa idea di sviluppo in progressione, grazie al fatto che la pianta romboidale occupa una superficie molto più ampia. Entrambi i progetti segnano l'inizio della costruzione dei ponti incaricati a Eiffel, e marcano inoltre il consolidamento della sua impresa, che iniziò dal disegno e dal cacolo delle strutture di una certa entità – 632 tonnellate il viadotto di Rouzat e 468 tonnellate quello di Neuvial.

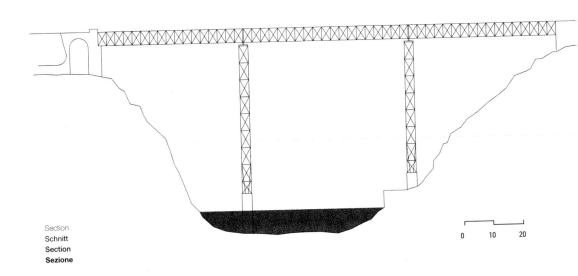

Section
Schnitt
Section
Sezione

0   10   20

Pedestrian Walkway in the Buttes-Chaumont Park

Rue Botzaris, Paris, France
1867

In 1867, the same year in which he would sign the contract to build the bridges in Neuvial and Rouzat, Eiffel obtained the concession to do the project for a metal walkway in the Buttes-Chaumont park north of Paris. This bridge, then, constitutes his first work in the French capital, but the popularity of this previously unknown engineer will not be slow to grow. The gardens of Buttes-Chaumont comprise a small recreational space that is very typical of the nineteenth century. The space is conceived through a picturesque prism and contains a large artificial lake with an island at its center. From this walkway, whose eight-meter height allows pedestrians an access to the island, one perceives a studied bucolic perspective that frames two rocky crags that flank the bridge as well as an arbor surrounded by lush vegetation. The piers of the bridge are anchored to some concrete blocks modeled in such a way as to appear to be of stone. This solution, perhaps today not very elegant was, in the nineteenth century, just one more of the park's attractions, given the novelty of the use of concrete.

1867 unterzeichnete Eiffel den Vertrag zum Bau der Brücken von Neuvial und Rouzat und erhielt noch im selben Jahr die Genehmigung zum Entwurf eines Laufstegs aus Metall im Park von Buttes-Chaumont nördlich von Paris. Diese Brücke war seine erste Arbeit in der französischen Hauptstadt, in der das Ansehen dieses unbekannten Ingenieurs jedoch rasch wuchs. Die Gärten von Buttes-Chaumont sind ein kleiner Erholungsraum mit einem überaus pittoresken Konzept, so wie es für das 19. Jahrhundert typisch ist. So befindet sich in ihnen ein künstlich angelegter See mit einer Insel in der Mitte. Von dem von Eiffel entworfenen, mehr als acht Meter hohen Laufsteg zur Insel aus blickt man über ein wohl durchdachtes bukolisches Panorama, das zwei Felsen zu beiden Seiten der Brücke und eine von üppiger Vegetation umgebene Laube enthält. Die Zuganker der Brücke liegen in Zementblöcken, die so modelliert wurden, dass sie wie Stein aussehen. Diese Lösung erscheint uns heute nicht eben elegant, war aber aufgrund des neuartigen Materials Mitte des 19. Jahrhunderts ein zusätzlicher Anziehungspunkt des Parks.

En 1867, l'année même de la signature du contrat de construction des ponts de Neuvial et Rouzat, Eiffel remporte la concession du projet d'une passerelle métallique dans le parc des Buttes-Chaumont, au nord de Paris. Ce pont lui offre son premier travail pour la capitale française, qui voit rapidement croître la popularité de cet ingénieur inconnu. Les jardins des Buttes-Chaumont constituent un petit espace de détente, typique du XIXème siècle, conçus dans une optique pittoresque et comptant un lac artificiel doté d'une île en son centre. Depuis la passerelle projetée par Eiffel, offrant une voie d'accès à l'île et dont la hauteur dépasse les huit mètres, il est possible d'appréhender une perspective bucolique très étudiée, embrassant deux parois rocheuses de part et d'autre du pont et une gloriette sous les frondaisons. Les montants du pont sont ancrés à des blocs de béton, moulés pour offrir l'apparence de la pierre. Il s'agit là d'une solution qui, bien que paraissant aujourd'hui peu élégante, offrait cependant au XIXème siècle un attrait supplémentaire au parc, de par la nouveauté du matériau employé.

Nel 1867, lo stesso anno in cui si firmò il contratto per la costruzione dei due ponti Neuvial e Rouzat, ottiene la concessione per progettare la passerella metallica del parco di Buttes-Chaumont, al nord di Parigi. Questo ponte costituisce il primo lavoro nella capitale francese, dove vede crescere rapidamente la sua popolarità di questo ingegnere sconosciuto. I giardini Buttes-Chaumont rappresentano una piccola area di ricreazione tipica del secolo XIX, concepita attraverso un sistema pintoresco, con laghi artificiali e una isola al centro. Dalla passerella progettata da Eiffel, grazie alla quale si raggiunge l'isola con 8 metri di altezza dal livello dell'acqua, si percepisce una studiata prospettiva bucolica che sottolinea due massi rocciosi che fiancheggiano il ponte e un pergolato circondato da una frondosa vegetazione. I tiranti del ponte sono ancorati a dei blocchi di cemento, modellati come se fossero pietre; una soluzione che, anche se oggi potrebbe apparire poco elegante, nella metà del secolo XIX rappresentava una delle attrazioni più spettacolari del parco.

Pedestrian Bridge in Girona

Hortes, Girona, Spain
1876–1877

At the close of the 1870s, the Eiffel Company came to Spain to build a series of small bridges for the rail system that linked the city of Girona with France. When, in 1876, the bidding was announced for a project for a walkway for pedestrians, Eiffel presented his design, which was realized a year later. This particular bridge is an example of the work method of the Eiffel Company: by working with standardized pieces, the manufacturing costs could be cut down, and this made it more competitive even than other companies located much closer to the work site than Eiffel, who shipped the material in from Paris. This mass-production style allowed the engineers to design small bridges in a short time because they already knew about all the elements. It was this kind of versatility that made it easy for Eiffel to build small bridges in practically any part of the world, all of them very similar. Later, in the decade of the 1880s, the company would begin to create portable bridges, when what was mass-produced was not limited to the pieces but extended to the whole assembly.

Ende der 1870er Jahre war Eiffels Unternehmen in Spanien tätig, um eine Reihe kleinerer Eisenbahnbrücken auf der Strecke zu bauen, die Girona mit Frankreich verband. Als 1876 das Projekt für einen Fußgängersteg innerhalb der Stadt ausgeschrieben wurde, reichte Eiffel seinen Entwurf ein und schloss die Arbeiten ein Jahr darauf ab. Die Brücke ist ein Beispiel für die Arbeitsweise der Firma Eiffels. Dadurch, dass er standardisierte Bauteile verwendete, konnte er die Herstellungskosten gering halten und war dadurch, obwohl er das Material aus Paris kommen ließ, wesentlich wettbewerbsfähiger als andere Unternehmen, die sich viel näher am Arbeitsort befanden. Diese Serienfertigung gestattete es den Ingenieuren auch, kleine Brücken in sehr kurzer Zeit zu entwerfen, da sie ja alle Komponenten von vornherein kannten. Aufgrund dieser Vielseitigkeit konnte Eiffel nahezu überall auf der Welt kleine Brücken bauen, die sich alle sehr ähnlich waren. Und noch später, in den 1880er Jahren, baute er sogar tragbare Brücken, bei denen sich die Serienfertigung nicht nur auf die einzelnen Bauteile beschränkte, sondern das gesamte Bauwerk umfasste.

La fin des années 70 du XIXème siècle découvre la société Eiffel en Espagne, chargée de construire une série de petits ponts pour la ligne ferroviaire reliant la ville de Girone à la France. Dans le cadre du concours de 1876 d'un projet de passerelle piétonnière au cœur de la ville, la société a présenté une création réalisée un an plus tard. Ce pont constitue un bon exemple de la méthode de travail de la société Eiffel : l'œuvre, incluant des pièces standardisées, permettait de minimiser les coûts de fabrication, devenant plus compétitive que celle d'autres entreprises plus proches du site des travaux, bien qu'acheminant les matériaux depuis Paris. Le travail en série offrait également aux ingénieurs la possibilité de concevoir des petits ponts en peu de temps, puisque ignorant à l'avance l'ensemble des données de terrain. Cette polyvalence facilita pour Eiffel la construction de petits ponts, tous très similaires, dans pratiquement dans tous les endroits du globe. Et plus tard, elle déboucherait sur la création de ponts portables, dans les années 80 du XIXème siècle, qui verraient la standardisation non seulement des pièces mais aussi des œuvres.

Al finale degli anni settanta, la società di Eiffel si trovava in Spagna per la costruzione di una serie di piccoli ponti per la linea ferroviaria che univa Girona con la Francia. Nel 1876, quando venne pubblicato il bando di concorso per il progetto di una passerella pedonale nella città di Girona, la società presenta la sua proposta, che venne realizzata un anno più tardi. Questo progetto costituisce un esemplare della metodologia di lavoro della sua compagnia: nel trattare pezzi standardizzati riesce a minimizzare i costi di produzione, il che lo rende competitivo con le altre imprese locali, ubicate molto più vicino al luogo di progetto rispetto alla sua, che si trovava obbligata nell'inviare i pezzi da Parigi. Questa standardizzazione permise inoltre agli ingegneri di disegnare piccoli ponti in poco tempo, partendo dal fatto che questi conoscessero tutti gli elementi che servivano per la costruzione. Questa versatilità facilita a Eiffel la costruzione di piccoli ponti in praticamente qualsìasi parte del mondo, molto simili tra loro. E questo lo porterà più avanti alla creazione di ponti portatili, negli anni ottanta, dove la serializzazione non si riduce solamente ai singoli pezzi ma a tutto il complesso.

Garabit Viaduct

Garabit, France
1879–1880

The bridge that Eiffel had built in Oporto was a much-admired project among the engineers of the time. This was true to such an extent that, in 1878, Léon Boyer imitated his solutions when designing the general layout of the Marvejols-Neussargues Line in order to span the huge gap of the Truyère River at Garabit. The State had in fact previously contracted the Eiffel company to build the viaduct itself without public bidding. The original sketch by Boyer was modified by the Eiffel team, with the young engineer Kœchlin at its head. It was then adapted to the specific needs of the terrain. Among the many changes the initial design underwent was the protection of the deck with a support structure to avoid possible destabilization of the train due to the strong winds that afflict the region. Additionally, the arch was changed from circular to parabolic, the auxiliary columns were moved closer to the keystone, and openwork beams were inserted to make revision and maintenance easier. This thorough refurbishment meant that the bridge would cease being a mere copy of the one at Oporto and become another Eiffel milestone.

Die Brücke, die Eiffel in Porto gebaut hatte, wurde von sämtlichen zeitgenössischen Ingenieuren sehr bewundert, was dazu führte, dass im Jahre 1878 Léon Boyer die in jenem Projekt verwendeten Lösungen kopierte, als er die allgemeine Führung der Strecke Marvejols-Neussargues plante. Hierbei musste auf der Höhe von Garabit eine tiefe Schlucht über den Truyère überbrückt werden. Der Staat nahm jedoch für die Verwirklichung dieses Viadukts Eiffels Gesellschaft selbst ohne vorherige öffentliche Ausschreibung unter Vertrag. Das Team Eiffels unter der Führung des jungen Ingenieurs Kœchlin änderte die ursprüngliche Struktur von Boyer ab und passte diese an die besonderen Erfordernisse des Baugrunds an. Eine dieser zahlreichen Änderungen bestand in einer Schutzkonstruktion für die Fahrbahn zu dem Zweck, das Abstürzen der Züge aufgrund der heftigen Winde zu verhindern, die in dieser Region wehen. Weiterhin wurde die runde Form des Bogens durch eine parabelförmige ersetzt, die Hilfspfeiler wurden an den Schlussstein des Bogens angenähert und aus durchbrochenen Balken gefertigt, um ihre Wartung und Instandhaltung zu erleichtern. Nach dieser umfassenden Überarbeitung war die Brücke von Garabit nicht mehr nur eine reine Kopie derjenigen von Porto und Eiffel setzte mit ihr einen weiteren Meilenstein.

Le pont construit par Eiffel à Porto devint un objet d'admiration pour tous les ingénieurs de l'époque, au point que, en 1878, Léon Boyer imita ses solutions lors de la conception du tracé général de la ligne Marvejols-Neussargues, afin de franchir la profonde gorge de la Truyère, à hauteur de Garabit. L'État attribua, sans concours préalable, le contrat à la société Eiffel pour la réalisation de la viaduc. L'idée d'origine de Boyer fut modifiée par l'équipe Eiffel – avec à sa tête le jeune ingénieur Kœchlin – et adaptée aux impératifs spécifiques du terrain. Parmi les nombreuses modifications de la conception initiale, l'on peut noter la protection de la voie par une structure de support, afin d'éviter la chute possible du train en raison de la force des vents balayant la région. Par surcroît, l'arche circulaire devint parabolique, les piliers auxiliaires se rapprochèrent de la clé de voûte et des poutrelles ajourées furent ajoutées afin d'en faciliter le contrôle et l'entretien. Suite à cette révision exhaustive, le pont de Garabit n'était plus une simple copie de celui de Porto mais bien un nouveau succès d'Eiffel.

Il ponte che Eiffel aveva costruito a Oporto era il risultato di un progetto molto ammirato da tutti gli ingegneri dell'epoca, fino al punto che, nel 1878 Léon Boyer imitò le sue soluzioni quando disegnò il tracciato generale della linea Marvejols-Neussargues per salvare la gola profonda del fiume Truyère, all'altezza del Garabit. Lo stato contrattò senza chiamata a bando la società di Eiffel per la realizzazione dil viadotto. L'idea originaria di Boyer venne modificata dalla compagnia di Eiffel – con a capo il giovane ingegnere Kœchlin – e venne adattato alle specifiche esigenze del terreno. Tra gli innumerevoli cambi che il ponte subì il progetto originario, si riscontra la protezione della via con una struttura di supporto, per evitare una possibile caduta del treno dovuta ai forti venti che interessano la regione. Inoltre l'arco si trasformò da circolare a parabolico, si avvicinarono i pilastri ausiliari verso la chiave di volta dell'arco e si eressero travi per facilitare la sua revisione e mantenimento. Dopo questo esaustivo cambiamento, il ponte del Garabit smise di essere una mera copia del ponte di Oporto, ma costituì un nuovo simbolo per Eiffel.

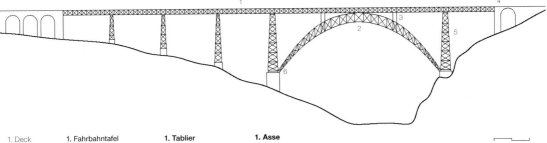

1. Deck	1. Fahrbahntafel	1. Tablier	1. Asse
2. Keystone	2. Schlussstein des Bogens	2. Clé de voûte	2. Chiave di volta
3. Support	3. Stützpfeiler	3. Montant	3. Montante
4. Buttress	4. Widerlager	4. Arc-boutant	4. Spalla del ponte
5. Column	5. Pfeiler	5. Pilier	5. Pilone
6. Rotation joint	6. Kugelgelenk	6. Rotule d'articulation	6. Ingranaggio di articolazione

0   20   40

Cubzac Bridge

Libourne, France
1879–1880

In 1879, Eiffel obtained the bid to remodel the Cubzac Bridge, located on the road between this town and Bordeaux. The project foresaw a structure of 553 meters in a straight line, with steel lattices. It would substitute an old viaduct that had been built in 1837. The designer of the project, the engineer of bridges and roads Sansac, wished to conserve the openwork iron columns of the old piece to cut costs and accelerate work. Hence, Eiffel decided to construct the two center sections without scaffolding and raise the bridge with an overhang. Thus, after the assembly of each beamed section, the workers would be working right atop them to construct the next interval. This would be continued right up to the final column. To join them, the overhanging section was raised with hydraulic jacks and thus corrected the structure's tension. Eiffel claimed to be the first to apply this method in France, using the qualities of the iron to flex it—unlike stone, which can only be worked in compression. This makes it possible to process a piece that has just been assembled, something impossible with pre-stressed concrete.

1879 erhielt Eiffel den Zuschlag für den Umbau der Brücke von Cubzac auf der Landstraße, die dieses Dorf mit Bordeaux verbindet. Der Entwurf sah eine 553 Meter lange geradlinige Struktur in Fachwerkbauweise vor, die das alte, 1837 erbaute Viadukt ersetzen sollte. Der zuständige Architekt, der Brücken- und Straßenbauingenieur Sansac, wollte die gusseisernen Pfeiler der alten Brücke erhalten, um die Kosten gering zu halten und die Bauarbeiten zu beschleunigen. Angesichts solcher Vorbedingungen beschloss Eiffel, die beiden mittleren Teilstücke ohne Baugerüst zu bauen und die Brücke im Freivorbauverfahren zu errichten. Jeweils nach Beendigung der Montage eines Teilträgers begaben sich die Arbeiter auf diesen, um von dort aus das nächste Teilstück anzubringen, und arbeiteten sich auf diese Weise bis zum nächsten Pfeiler vor. Um die Teile zu verbinden, musste das vorkragende Stück mittels hydraulischer Kräne angehoben werden, um so die Biegung der Struktur zu korrigieren. Eiffel nahm für sich in Anspruch, der erste Ingenieur zu sein, der diese Bauweise in Frankreich anwendete. Durch sie wurden die Eigenschaften des Eisens ausgenutzt, das im Unterschied zum Stein, der lediglich unter Druck formbar ist, unter Biegen verarbeitet werden kann. Außerdem konnte ein gerade zusammengefügtes Teil unverzüglich weiterverarbeitet werden, was bei Stahlbeton undenkbar war.

En 1879, Eiffel emporte la rénovation du pont de Cubzac, sur la route reliant la ville à Bordeaux. Le projet prévoyait une structure rectiligne de 553 mètres, un réticule de poutrelles, devant se substituer à l'ancien viaduc datant de 1837. Son créateur, l'ingénieur des ponts et chaussées Sansac, souhaitait préserver les piliers métalliques pour réduire les coûts et accélérer les travaux. Face à de telles prémisses, Eiffel décidait de construire les deux tronçons centraux sans échafaudage, pour construire le pont en porte-à-faux : après la fin de l'assemblage de chaque tronçon, les ouvriers l'utilisaient pour assembler l'intervalle suivant, progressant ainsi pour atteindre l'autre pile. Pour les réunir, il fut nécessaire de hisser la partie en porte-à-faux au moyen de vérins hydrauliques, corrigeant ainsi le fléchissement de la structure. Eiffel revendiquait être le premier ingénieur appliquant cette technique de construction en France, un système mettant à profit les propriétés du fer : travail en flexion – à la différence de la pierre, travaillant uniquement en compression – et travail immédiat sur une pièce tout juste assemblée – inenvisageable avec le béton armé par exemple.

Nel 1879 Eiffel ottiene l'aggiudicazione della rimodellazione del ponte di Cubzac, nella strada che unisce il villaggio con Bordeaux. Il progetto prevede una struttura di 553 metri in linea retta, in travi reticolari che devono sostituitre l'antico viadotto costruito nel 1837. Il suo progettista, l'ingegnere civile Sansac, voleva conservare i pilastri di ferro fuso per arrotondare i costi e accelerare i lavori. Con queste premesse Eiffel decise di costruire i due trami centrali senza impalcature ed erigere il ponte in aggetto: nel momento di terminare il montaggio delle travi dei due trami, gli operai dovettero lavorare in cima di queste per armare il seguente intervallo, procedendo in questo modo fino ad arrivare al seguente pilastro. Per unirli fu necessario erigere il tramo in aggetto mediante martinetti idraulici e correggere in questo modo la flessione della struttura. Eiffel rivendicò essere il primo ingegnere ad aver usato questo metodo costruttivo in tutta Francia, un sistema mediante il quale si sfruttano al massimo le potenzialità del ferro, che può lavorare a flessione a differenza della pietra, può lavorare a compressione e permette di operare direttamente con un pezzo terminato che serve per l'assemblaggio, cosa impossibile per il cemento armato.

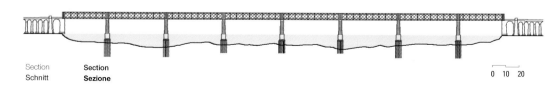

Section   Section
Schnitt   Sezione

0 10 20

Viaduct across the Tardes River

Evaux-les-Bains, France
1881–1884

In 1881 Eiffel won the bid to build a viaduct over the Tardes River, near the town of Evaux-les-Bains. The new structure was to span a very deep chasm. In the platform design, a multiple lattice that included no vertical support, he applied the same system of construction of the overhanging sections that had already been used on the bridge built at Cubzac. However, the new project presented here had much larger dimensions: the columns measured nearly 60 meters in height and the grade difference in the center was over 100 meters. The bridge would have to span a gap of 250 meters, divided into three sections (73, 104, and 73 meters). Also foreseen were two large piers to support the deck. At the end of January 1884, after a section of 54 meters had been erected in overhang, and after three weeks of work, an extremely high wind flattened the metallic structure. The accident was considered due to force majeure and the State assumed the damages; but the experience sparked in Eiffel a passion that would remain: the study of wind, thus making him one of the pioneers of aerodynamics.

1881 gewann Eiffel den Wettbewerb zur Errichtung eines Viadukts über die tiefe Schlucht des Tardes, der in der Nähe der Ortschaft Evaux-les-Bains fließt. Beim Entwurf für das Bauwerk wandte er die gleiche Bauweise vorgefertigter Teilstrecken an wie bei der Brücke von Cubzac. Diesmal waren allerdings die Dimensionen des Projekts wesentlich größer, die Baupfeiler hatten eine Höhe von fast 60 Metern und der Höhenunterschied in der Mitte betrug mehr als 100 Meter. Die Brücke sollte eine Länge von 250 Metern überspannen, die auf drei Teile von jeweils 73, 104 und 73 Metern aufgeteilt war, und es waren zwei große Pfeiler vorgesehen, welche die Fahrbahntafel tragen sollten. Ende Januar 1884 war in dreiwöchiger Arbeit vom Pfeiler des rechten Ufers ausgehend bereits ein 54 Meter langes Teilstück vorgebaut worden, als ein gewaltiger Sturm die gesamte Metallstruktur niederriss. Es wurde zwar höhere Gewalt geltend gemacht und der Staat kam für die entstandenen Schäden auf, aber das Erlebnis weckte in Gustave Eiffel eine Leidenschaft, die ihn sein ganzes Leben lang begleiten sollte. Es handelte sich um das Studium des Windes und er wurde zu einem der Pioniere auf dem Gebiet der Aerodynamik.

En 1881, Eiffel gagnait le concours de construction d'un viaduc sur la rivière Tardes, proche d'Evaux-les-Bains, afin de franchir une gorge profonde. Sa conception de plate-forme rectiligne à réticules multiples, sans armatures verticales, se vit appliquée le même concept de tronçons en porte-à-faux, déjà utilisé pour le pont de Cubzac, même si le projet affichait une ampleur supérieure : les piles du pont s'élevaient de 60 mètres et le dénivelé central dépassait les 100 mètres. Le pont devait courir sur une longueur de 250 mètres, répartis en trois parties de 73, 104 et 73 mètres, deux grands piliers étant prévus pour soutenir le tablier. Fin janvier 1884, un tronçon de 54 mètres en porte-à-faux ayant été érigé depuis la pile de la rive droite, après trois de semaines de labeur, de puissantes rafales de vent emportaient complètement la structure métallique. L'accident fut imputé à un cas de force majeure et l'État pris les dégâts à sa charge. Cependant l'événement éveilla chez Gustave Eiffel une passion qui l'accompagnerait toute sa vie, l'étude des vents, et le convertirait en l'un des pionniers de l'aérodynamique.

Nel 1881 Eiffel vince il concorso per la costruzione di un viadotto sul fiume Tardes, vicino alla località Evaux-les-Bains, il cui compito era quello di ricucire la profonda gola. Nel suo progetto di piattaforma retta reticolare multiple senza armatura verticale, applicò lo stesso sistema costruttivo dei trami a sbalzo che aveva già utilizzato per il ponte di Cubzac, anche se la nuova proposta presentava delle dimensioni alquanto maggiori: i pilastri della impalcatura raggiungevano quasi i 60 metri in altezza mentre la quota di dislivello nel centro superava i 100 metri. Il ponte doveva coprire una luce di 250 metri, divisa in tre trami di 73, 104 e 73 metri, e si prevederono due grandi pilastri per reggere l'impalcatura. Alla fine del gennaio del 1884, dopo aver eretto il tramo di 54 metri di aggetto che sosteneva il pilastro della sponda destra e dopo tre settimane di lavoro, un fortissimo uragano sradicò totalmente la struttura metallica. L'incidente venne considerato causa di forza maggiore e lo Stato ne assunse i danni, ma la vivacità intellettuale di Eiffel risvegliò in lui la passione che lo accompagnò per tutta la vita: lo studio del vento, che lo convertì in uno dei pionieri dell'aerodinàmica.

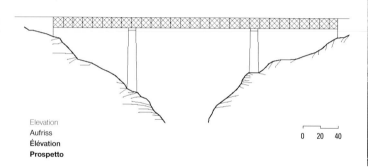

Elevation
Aufriss
Élévation
Prospetto

0 20 40

Observatory at Nice

Grande Corniche, Mont Gros, Nice, France
1885–1886

At the end of the nineteenth century, the progress of the study of astronomy required ever larger telescopes. These, at the same time, needed to be protected by large domes that would permit their mobility in order to scan the celestial hemisphere. In 1881, Gustave Eiffel participated in the bidding for the remodeling work on the dome of the Paris observatory. His design was a patented project that situated the dome on a lubricated antifreezing magnesium chloride circular rail. Eiffel did not win the bid, but his solution struck the attention of some of the jury members and also that of Charles Garnier who, some years later, required Eiffel's services for the observatory at Nice. This structure was fitted with a telescope 18 meters in length and a roof 22,40 meters in diameter. The dome assembly was concluded in 1886, and it showed that a single person could move its 100 tons using only one hand. The building, designed by Garnier himself, combines powerful wall with simple Ionic columns. And it serves as a base for Eiffel's dome, which rises up on it majestically, as if in defiance of gravity itself.

Gegen Ende des 19. Jahrhunderts machten die Fortschritte der astronomischen Forschung immer größere Teleskope notwendig, die ihrerseits von großen Kuppeln geschützt werden mussten. Diese mussten beweglich sein, um den gesamten Himmel über einer Hemisphäre zu erfassen. Im Jahre 1881 nahm Gustave Eiffel an einem Wettbewerb für den Umbau der Kuppel des Observatoriums von Paris teil. Er stellte dafür einen patentierten Entwurf vor, bei dem der bewegliche Dom auf einer ringförmigen, mit gefrierfestem Magnesiumchlorid gefüllten Bahn glitt. Damit gewann er zwar nicht den Wettbewerb, aber seine Lösung erweckte die Aufmerksamkeit einiger Mitglieder der Jury sowie die Charles Garniers. Dieser bat ihn Jahre später um seine Dienste für das Observatorium von Nizza, das mit einem 18 Meter langen Teleskop und einer Kuppel mit einem Durchmesser von 22,40 Metern ausgestattet war. Die Montage der Kuppel war 1886 beendet und bewies, dass ihr Gewicht von hundert Tonnen von einem einzigen Menschen mit nur einer Hand bewegt werden konnte. Garnier selbst hatte das Gebäude entworfen, das eine starke Mauer mit einfachen ionischen Säulen kombiniert und als Sockel für die Kuppel Eiffels dient, die sich über diesen mächtigen Unterbau majestätisch und nahezu schwerelos erhebt.

À la fin du XIXème siècle, les progrès des études astronomiques étaient tels que la science requérait l'installation de télescopes sans cesse plus grands, devant être à leur tour protégés par de vastes coupoles, mobiles afin de capter l'ensemble de l'hémisphère céleste. En 1881, Gustave Eiffel participait au concours de rénovation de la coupole de l'observatoire de Paris, avec un projet breveté qui situait le dôme sur une voie annulaire remplie de chlorure de magnésium antigel, facilitant son glissement. Eiffel ne remporta pas le concours mais sa solution suscita l'intérêt de certains membres du jury ainsi que l'attention de Charles Garnier qui, quelques années plus tard, s'attacha ses services pour l'observatoire de Nice, doté d'un télescope de 18 mètres de long et d'une coupole de 22,40 mètres de diamètre. Le montage de la coupole se termina en 1886 et apporta la preuve qu'une personne seule pouvait déplacer cent tonnes d'une seule main. Le bâtiment, conçu par Garnier lui-même, alliait un mur imposant à des colonnes ioniques simples et offrait son assise à la coupole d'Eiffel, s'élevant majestueuse, voire légère, sur cette base omnipotente.

Alla fine del XIX° secolo il progresso nello studio dell'astronomia richiedeva l'istallazione di telescopi sempre più grandi, e a loro volta dovevano essere protetti da grandi cupole, che dovevano essere mobili per permettere di captare tutto l'emisfero celeste. Nel 1881 Eiffel partecipò al concorso di ristrutturazione della cupola dell'osservatorio di Parigi, con un progetto patentato che situava la cupola su un binario anulare pieno di cloruro di magnesio anticongelante che facilitava il suo scorrimento. Eiffel vinse il concorso, ma la sua soluzione chiamò l'attenzione di alcuni membri della giuria e anche quella di Charles Garnier che, alcuni anni dopo, richiese il suo lavoro per l'osservatorio di Nizza, dotato di un telescopio di 18 metri di altezza e di una cupola di 22,40 metri di diametro. Il montaggio della cupola si concluse nel 1886, e dimostrò che una sola persona poteva muovere 100 tonnellate con una sola mano. L'edificio, disegnato dallo stesso Garnier, combina un muro imponente con delle semplici colonne ioniche, e serve come podio alla cupola di Eiffel, la quale, sopra questa poderosa base si alza maestosa, addirittura in tutta la sua forza.

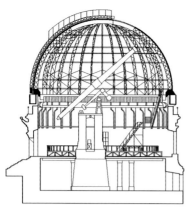

Longitudinal section
Längsschnitt
Section longitudinale
Sezione longitudinale

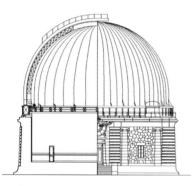

Cross section
Querschnitt
Section transversale
Sezione trasversale

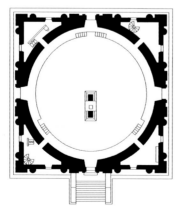

Plan
Grundriss
Niveau
Pianta

0　3　6

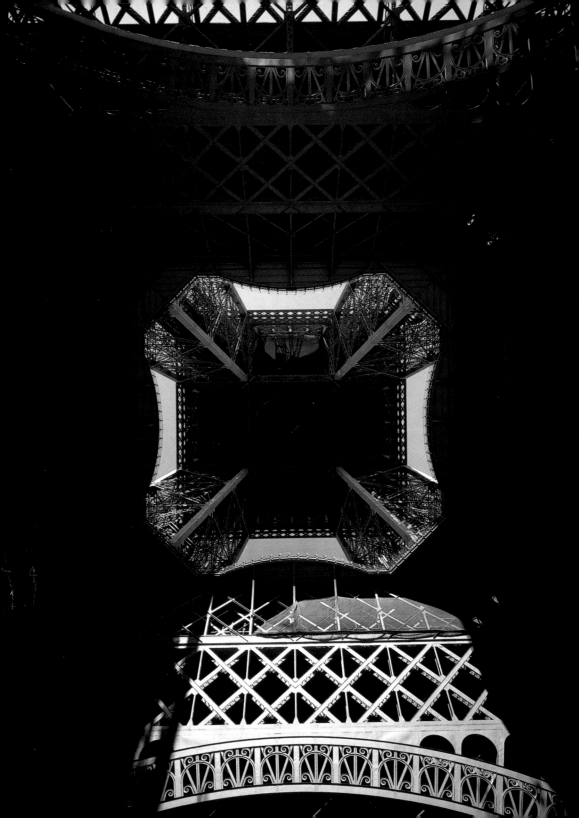

Eiffel Tower

Champ de Mars, Paris, France
1884–1889

The idea of raising a building over a thousand feet high had already been studied in Europe and the United States but without success. Nougier and Kœchlin researched the viability of putting up a tower with prospect of the Universal Exposition of 1889, which was to commemorate the first centenary of the French Revolution. But Eiffel could muster no interest in the project until he realized that there would be a good deal of prestige to be culled from being the creator of the tallest building in the world, from whose top floor the French tricolor would fly. With this aim in mind, he invested part of his personal fortune and convinced the authorities of the advantages of his structure. The tower, which took 26 months to erect—twice the estimated time—had three stories. The arch that apparently supports the first level in fact serves no structural function whatsoever. It is merely the main decorative element, in advance of the Art Nouveau of century's end. The structure has seven stairways, four of which are spiral, and five elevators. It took 9,000 tons of iron to finish the job.

Der Versuch, ein mehr als tausend Fuß hohes Gebäude zu errichten, war bereits ohne Erfolg in Europa und in den Vereinigten Staaten unternommen worden. Nougier und Kœchlin, zwei Ingenieure aus Eiffels Unternehmen, untersuchten die technische Realisierbarkeit des Baus eines Eisenturms im Hinblick auf die Weltausstellung von 1889, die zum Gedenken an den hundertsten Jahrestag der Französischen Revolution stattfinden sollte. Eiffel jedoch interessierte sich nicht für das Projekt, bis er schließlich feststellte, welch großes Prestige es für ihn bedeuten würde, der Vater des höchsten Bauwerks der Welt zu sein, auf dessen Spitze die Trikolore im Wind wehen würde. Mit dieser Absicht investierte er einen Teil seines Privatvermögens in das Vorhaben und unternahm alles nur Mögliche, um die zuständigen Behörden von den Vorzügen seines Entwurfs zu überzeugen. Der Turm, dessen Bauzeit mit 26 Monaten doppelt so lang wie ursprünglich geplant war, besteht aus drei Stockwerken. Der Bogen, der scheinbar die erste Ebene trägt, besitzt tatsächlich keinerlei tragende Funktion und ist das hauptsächliche dekorative Element, das den Art Nouveau der Jahrhundertwende vorwegnimmt. Der Komplex verfügt über sieben Treppen, darunter vier Wendeltreppen, sowie fünf Aufzüge, und für seinen Bau waren insgesamt 9000 Tonnen Eisen nötig.

L'idée d'ériger un édifice de plus de mille pieds avait déjà fait l'objet de conjectures en Europe et aux États-Unis, mais sans succès. Nougier et Kœchlin – deux ingénieurs d'Eiffel – étudièrent la viabilité technique de la construction d'une tour d'acier, avec à l'esprit l'Exposition universelle de 1889, qui devait commémorer le premier centenaire de la Révolution française. Il faut noter qu'Eiffel s'intéressa au projet seulement lorsqu'il prit conscience du prestige que pourrait lui apporter son soutien à la construction la plus élevée du monde, dont la cime serait ornée du drapeau tricolore. À cet effet, il investit une partie de sa fortune particulière et se lança dans une série d'activités destinées à convaincre les autorités de ses avantages. La tour, qui devrait attendre 26 mois avant la conclusion des travaux – le double du délai estimé – comportait trois niveaux : l'arche supportant apparemment le premier étage n'a aucune fonction structurelle réelle et constitue l'élément décoratif principal, annonçant l'Art Nouveau de la fin du siècle. L'ensemble propose sept escaliers – quatre en colimaçon – et 5 ascenseurs et requit 9 000 tonnes d'acier pour son achèvement.

L'idea di erigere un edificio di più di mille piedi già era stata presa in considerazione dall'europa e dagli stati Uniti, ma senza esito. Nougier e Kœchlin, due ingegneri di Eiffel, studiarono la fattibilità tecnica di erigere una torre in ferro con l'obiettivo dell'Esposizione Universale del 1889, che commemorava il primo centenario della Rivoluzione Francese. Non ostante questo Eiffel non si interessò del progetto fino a quando si rese conto del prestigio che poteva recargli un edificio più alto del mondo, la cui cima sarebbe stata incoronata dalla bandiera tricolore del suo paese. Con questo obiettivo investì parte della sua fortuna personale e invertì azioni destinate a persuadere le autorità pertinenti sul valore e vantaggio dell'opera. La torre, che venne costruita in 26 mesi, ossia il doppio del tempo stimato, è costituita da tre piani. L'arco che apparentemente regge il primo livello non riveste alcuna funzione strutturale ma costituisce l'elemento decorativo principale, che anticipa l'Art Nouveau di fine secolo. Il complesso dispone di sette corpi scala e quattro di queste sono a chiocciola, di cinque ascensori e furono necessarie 9.000 tonnellate di ferro per terminarlo.

Elevation
Aufriss
Élévation
Prospetto

0 2 4

Chronology of Eiffel's works

1832	Birth at Dijon, France, December 15.
1852–1855	Obtains his engineering diploma (specialization in chemistry) at the Ecole Central de Paris, France.
1856	Meets Nepveu. Eiffel works for some months in the rail company Western Railroads, then enters the Pauwels and Co. Society, Paris, France.
1857–1860	Builds Saint Jean bridge across the Garonne River in Bordeaux, France.
1864	Founds his own company in Paris, France.
1866–1867	Builds the roofs for the synagogue on the rue des Tournelles, Paris, France.
	Bridges on the Poitiers-Limoges Line, France.
	Church of Notre-Dame des Champs, Paris, France.
1867	Pedestrian Walkway, Buttes-Chaumont Park, Paris, France.
1868–1869	Bridge across the Marne, Château-Thierry, France.
	Gas company in Poissy, Vaugirard and Ternes, France.
1869	Viaducts of Rouzat and Neuvial, France.
1870	Bridges on the Latour-sur-Orb Line in Millau, France.
	Bridges on the Brive-Tulle Line, France.
1872	Bridges on the Vendée Line, France.
	Bridge across the Thouet River in Thouars, across the Cher River in Tours, and across the Indré River in Azay-le-Rideau, France.
	Customs building and docks, Arica, Chile.
1873–1874	Gas company, La Paz, Bolivia.
	Lycée Carnot, Paris, France.
1875	Church in Manila, Philippines; in Tacna, Peru, and in Arica, Chile.
	Casino de Sables-d'Olonne, France.
1875–1877	Nyugati Station, Nyugati, Hungary.
	María Pía Bridge across the Duero River, Portugal.
1876–1877	Gas company in la Villette and in Ivry, France.
	Kay in Chala, Peru.
	Bridges on the Girona Line, France.

	Pedestrian bridge in Girona, Spain.
1877–1878	Bridges across Miño River, Spain.
1878	Pavilion of the City of Paris; pavilion of the Paris gas company for the Universal Exposition, France.
	Gas company, Clichy, France.
1879–1880	Annex to the Louvre storerooms, Paris, France.
	Au Bon Marché warehouse, Paris, France.
	Roadway bridges in Campina, Rumania; Oued Djemma, Algeria; Savon-Nieres and St. Laurent-sur-Sevres, France.
	Bridges on the Beira Alta Line, Portugal.
	Roadway bridge Cubzac, France.
	Viaduct Garabit, France.
1881	Railroad stations, San Sebastián and Santander, Spain.
	Crèdit Lyonnais, Paris, France.
1881–1884	Viaduct across the Tardes River in Evaux-les-Bains, France.
1881–1886	Structure for the Statue of Liberty, New York City, USA.
1882	Bridges on the Asturias, Galicia and Leon railway, Spain.
1883	Portable bridges, Senegal.
1884–1889	Eiffel Tower, Paris, France.
1885	Bridges and stations on the Lisboa-Sintra Line, Portugal.
1885–1886	Observatory dome, Nice, France.
1887	Locks for the Panama Canal.
1890	Project for the Paris metro, Paris, France.
	Project for the tunnel under the English Channel, France–United Kingdom.
1893	Opening of the trial of the administrators of the Panama Canal Company.
	Eiffel resigns his post; Kœchlin becomes president.
1912	Aerodynamic laboratory, Paris, France.
1917	Airplane prototype.
1923	Death in Paris at the age of 89.

Acknowledgements

We remain grateful to the Société Nouvelle d'Exploitation de la Tour Eiffel, and especially to Stéphane Dieu, and to all of other official institutions who gave us their assistance.